TAKING IT FROM THE TOP

THE SITE FOR THE EDEN PROJECT, 1998

We recycle all our rubbish. Help us by putting things in the right bins. Thanks.

WHY A PROJECT?

Eden is a project because we're always trying out new things that help look after the planet (and sharing what we find out). Tell us your ideas too!

BEFORE ALAN AND ENID ARRIVED

In 1998 this place was a soggy clay pit: no paths, no plants, no buildings, no soil. Our Eden team made it into a global garden to show what a group of people can do if they really believe it's possible.

WHY PLANTS?

In our garden we show you the plants that make our food, fuel, medicines and materials. We show ways of looking after these plants, the people that grow them and the planet. They all look after us!

Our plants are watered and loos flushed with rainwater.

THE EDEN PROJECT SITE, 2002

DIGGER THE DOG...

Digger loves food. Join him on the food trail to meet the plants that make your food. Look out for this symbol on site and on the map.

Collect the stamps above in your book on pages 5, 9, 17, 23, 25, 37 and 39. Solve the riddles on the trail and send the answers to Digger, Eden Project, Bodelva, Cornwall, PL24 2SG. Winners of the monthly prize draw are posted on **www.edenproject.com**.

LOOK OUT FOR THE STAMP BLOCKS AND STAMP YOUR BOOK LIKE EANNA HERE

AND SNIFF THE CAT

There's always something we can do to help out.

Meet Sniff, a cat on a mission. She's hunting out ideas that could help Alan and Enid – in fact all of us – look after the planet that looks after us. Send Sniff your ideas at the address on the left or email **sniff@edenproject.com**.

THE OUTDOOR BIOME

GO DOWN THE ZIGZAG PATH, PAST AGE-OLD FERNS TO THE WEEEMAN AND THE CROPS THAT FEED THE

THE OUTDOOR BIOME

EXPLORE!

Help Alan and Enid find plants that make tea, rope, oils, breakfast cereals, bread, popcorn, fuel.

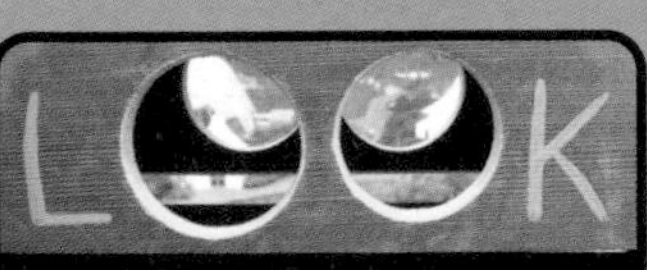

HAVE A LOOK THROUGH THE FENCE

PLANTS AROUND IN DINOSAUR-TIMES ROTTED TO MAKE COAL

FLOWERLESS GARDEN (0.02)

Burning fossil fuels (coal, petrol, diesel) releases CO_2 that's been stored underground for millions of years back into the air. This forms a gassy blanket around the Earth, contributing to climate change.

Our land train runs on biofuel made from plants. This doesn't increase CO_2 levels. Good for the climate!

WORLD. LOOK OUT FOR PLANTS FOR FOOD, FUEL, MEDICINES, MATERIALS.

THE WEEEMAN

This robot is made of all the Waste Electrical and Electronic Equipment we throw away in our lives. So look after stuff: fix it, don't chuck it.

THE BIG WEEEMAN

DIGGER ASKS

What six crops feed most of the people in the world?
Rice, potatoes, bananas, beans, _ _ _ _ _ and _ _ _ _ _.
Find the answers by working out the riddles on the food trail posts, send them in with your other riddle answers (to the address on page 2) to enter the grand draw.

WHEAT

(0.03)

Wheat flour can be made into tasty bread, cakes and breakfast cereals. Durum wheat is made into pasta.

WHEAT

FOOD TRAIL

0.03

0.03

PAST THE FLOWERS AND SWEET PEA FENCE TO THE MAIN GARDEN WITH ITS MAGICAL OUTDOOR ROOMS

TIME TO RELAX...

DRAW YOUR FAVOURITE THING IN THE GARDEN

FLOWERS IN THE MAKING

(0.04)

In the summer there are plenty of colours here to brighten up Alan and Enid's vase.

THE GARDEN

(0.05)

A place to run, jump, explore, have an adventure, share with friends (and wildlife), grow food and sniff flowers. Draw a picture of your favourite thing in this garden.

Save water in the garden. How? Let's collect it off the roof and store it in a butt. Alan can water the plants and splash Digger with it. Just keep it off me!

STOP TO PLAY IN THE SANDPIT

PLAY (0.06)

Our play garden is made out of willow branches. You just push them into the ground and they grow roots. They are magic plants for making dens!

STOP OFF IN THE WILLOW PLAY AREA AND THEN ON TO THE CAFÉ BY PLANTS FOR TASTE.

. . . AND PLAY A GAME

PLANTS FOR TASTE (0.07)

The chefs use these herbs in the café. We can't grow enough vegetables to feed all the visitors so these are grown on local farms: less transportation, less lorries, less fumes, less CO_2, less climate change.

THE PLANTS FOR TASTE GARDEN

HEAD FOR THE BEE, THEN THE TEA SHIP VIA THE 'NEW USES FOR CROPS' EXHIBIT. LOOK OUT FOR

CROPS FOR PLASTICS AND PERFUMES

NEW USES FOR CROPS (0.08)

Plastic can be made from plants as well as from fossil fuels (oil from underground). Alan looks for plastic carrier bags and nappies made from maize and wax crayons made from soybeans.

So what? well, plants keep growing so we can keep making this plastic and it rots so it reduces rubbish.

LAVENDER BUSHES

FORKS MADE FROM MAIZE PLASTIC

LAVENDER (0.09)

Smells great in summer. Its name comes from the Latin 'lavare': to wash (so do the words laundry and lavatory).

POLLINATION (0.10)

- Bees pollinate flowers.
- Flowers reward the bees with nectar.
- They make it into honey.

The flowers growing here attract bees. How many sorts of flowers can you see?

THE GIANT BEE

FOOD AND DRINK

GLOBAL GARDENERS (0.14)

Find tips from gardeners worldwide and discover more about our Gardens for Life programme.

TEA (0.13)

Ah, time for a cuppa and a chance to find out about tea.

PLAY ON THE TEA SHIP

THE HOP POLES

BEER AND BREWING (0.12)

Find out the ingredients for beer in the hop poles.

DIGGER GOES CORNISH

These crops (0.11) grow earlier in Cornwall than in other parts of the UK because it's warmer down here. Which crops crop up in the answer to riddle 0.11? Now there's a real riddle in a riddle!

FOOD TRAIL

0.11

□□□□□

0.13

□□□

KEEP ON WALKING UP ... PEEP THROUGH THE HEMP FENCE. CHECK OUT THE OIL CROPS ON THE

ROPE AND OILS

HEMP (0.16)

Alan's delighted. He's found hemp, which can be made into clothes, oil, rope, fuel, paper and plastic. Here we've made it into a fence.

THE HEMP FENCE, A STRONG BARRIER MADE FROM PLANT STEMS

THE METAL GIANT

ROPE AND FIBRE (0.18)

Strong plant fibres make strong rope. How strong? Try tugging the giant.

DIGGER ON PLANT OILS (0.17)

I'm a bit of a health expert! I like sunflower oil. It's low in saturated fat and high in Vitamin E. They're cooking crisps in it these days instead of using palm oil. More on that later! In fact sunflower oil is SUCH good stuff that they sometimes use it to lubricate racing-car engines.

CORNER ... PAST THE METAL GIANT TO THE INDUSTRIAL FLAME PLANT.

KEEPING WARM, KEEPING COOL

INDUSTRIAL FLAME PLANT

FUEL (0.21)

Sniff says use plants like the ones here as fuel instead of using coal. Why? Because burning fossil fuels (like coal and oil and gas from underground) puts carbon dioxide (CO_2) into the air and adds to climate change.

PLANTS FOR A WARMER CLIMATE (0.20)

We took a very steep slope, with very little soil, baked by the sun, and found some plants that would grow here. Whatever the problem, there's always an answer if you really try!

GARDENING ON A STEEP SLOPE

UP AND UP TO WILD CORNWALL AND MINERALS. PHEW! MADE IT! WHERE DO YOU WANT TO GO NOW?

LOOKING AFTER LIFE

FOLLOW THE LABYRINTH IN THE DREAM CHAMBER

BIODIVERSITY AND CORNWALL (0.23)

Biodiversity means the variety of life: all the millions of different plants and animals in the world. Big or small they all play an important part. How many different Cornish wild plants can you spot up here in one minute: ☐

FROM THE EARTH (0.24)

We need mines for metals and rocks. Can you think of five useful things for Alan and Enid that are made out of metal or stone? Our Eden team work with people to help wild plants and animals move back in after mines have closed down.

MYTH (0.22)
Stories, play and using your imagination are vital! They help us understand things. They help us to care. Come on, Enid. Tell me a tale. puurrrrrr!

WHO LIVES IN HERE?

Look out for two more great outdoor pages in the Core section at the end of the book!

THE RAINFOREST BIOME

PHEW! COATS OFF . . . LOOK FOR THE MAP (ON THE LEFT) AND THE HUGE TROPIC TRADER SHIP ON YOUR RIGHT.

THE TROPIC TRADER

WELCOME, ALL, TO THE . . .

RAINFORESTS AND HUMID TROPICS REGIONS

Trek through the steamy rainforests and find the plants used by Alan, Enid and you from these parts of the world. Once brought on ships like the huge Tropic Trader, they now usually arrive by plane.

Save the rainforests: they help control the climate, cool the Earth, give us plants for food and medicines and make rain (hey, get me an umbrella!).

TROPICAL SOUTH AMERICA
WEST AFRICA
MALAYSIA
SEYCHELLES
ST HELENA

THE HUMID TROPICS REGIONS OF THE WORLD

SAVE THE RAINFOREST

If we were ancient Egyptians we'd be looking for PAPYRUS to write on. Which plant is it?
Where's the TRAVELLER'S PALM to point us in the right direction?
H.01
THEN GO PAST PAPYRUS AND THE REALLY BIG TRAVELLER'S PALM BEFORE YOU REACH THE BRIDGE . . .
DIGGER HUNTS OUT TROPICAL FOODS
There are four riddles and four stamps in this Biome. I know, 'Buy food from the UK', Sniff would say, but it's more complicated than that. What we can do is buy fairly traded foods from the tropics which gives a fair deal to the growers.
Which of these plants come from the humid tropics?
SUGAR CANE FOR SUGAR
LEMONS FOR LEMONADE
WHEAT FOR BREAD
GRAPES FOR WINE
COFFEE BEANS FOR COFFEE DRINKS
KIWI FRUIT FOR EATING
COCOA FOR CHOCOLATE BARS
BANANAS FOR THE FRUIT BOWL
MANGOES FOR SMOOTHIES
(Answers at the back of the book.)

CROSS THE BRIDGES AND FOLLOW THE WINDING PATH THROUGH THE TROPICAL ISLANDS ...

LET'S VISIT SOME TROPICAL PLACES

SAM THOMPSON HOLDING A COCO DE MER SEED

TROPICAL ISLANDS (H.02)

The tropics are home to rare wild plants like the Coco de Mer which are threatened by clearing land for roads, houses and crops, and increasing numbers of tourists. Eden works with scientists and local people in the Seychelles to save rare plants like this:

You can help save Balsamine sauvage too. Ask a member of the Eden team where you can find out about our Ray of Hope plants.

BALSAMINE SAUVAGE

YOUNG MANGROVES

THE MANGROVE SWAMP (H.02)

Mangroves grow in the mud between land and sea. They protect the coast from storms and help act as a natural barrier in tsunamis.

WALK ROUND THE HAIRPIN BEND AND UP INTO MALAYSIA.

THE MALAYSIAN GARDEN (H.03)

Enid likes the house. It's made out of plants and it's on stilts to keep clear of floods and snakes (don't worry, there are none in here). Alan recognizes the chillies and rice but isn't quite sure what the other plants are. Let's ask Digger!

HOT CHILLIES

MALAYSIAN HOUSE WITH KITCHEN GARDEN

DIGGER KNOWS HIS STUFF (H.03)

I know! These winged beans are like our runner beans. Pak choi is like cabbage, and people here eat rice instead of potatoes. It grows in the paddy near the food trail. Oops, give-away!

RICE

FOOD TRAIL

H.03

WHAT AM I?

I FEED OVER HALF THE WORLD:
I PROVIDE FOR PEOPLE'S NEEDS.
I'M A TYPE OF GRASS YOU SEE,
YOU OFTEN EAT MY SEEDS.

I'm looking for CASSAVA ROOTS. The leaves of this plant are like fingers.

I need PAPAYAS and MANGOES for the fruit bowl.

Many of these crops are trees. They make an edible rainforest! I'm going to get Alan to make an edible forest garden here in the UK using fruit trees and climbing beans!

ROUND THE ELBOW BEND TO THE POST THAT SAYS 'WEST AFRICA', THEN

FROM WEST AFRICA TO . . .

WEST AFRICAN TOTEMS

(H.04)

Why do they look burnt? Because the timber was recycled from a part of Falmouth docks which was destroyed by fire. They originally started their life as trees in West Africa!

TOTEMS BY WEST AFRICAN SCULPTOR, EL ANATSUI

WEST AFRICA

(H.04)

Local farmers grow crops that fertilize the soil, feed the people and can be sold at market.

PAPAYA TREE AND FRUIT

SOIL FEEDERS

(H.04)

These legume trees make plant fertilizer in their roots to feed the soil. The beans we grow in our gardens do that too.

LEGUME TREE

TAKE THE LOWER ROAD PAST THE COOL ROOM TO THE POST THAT SAYS 'SOUTH AMERICA'.

...TROPICAL SOUTH AMERICA

CASSAVA HOUSE

CASSAVA PLANT

CASSAVA (H.05)

In South America, local people eat a lot of cassava. The thick roots are grated and washed and a paste is squeezed out in 'tipitis'.

DIGGER ON CASSAVA (H.05)

Have you ever eaten tapioca? It's made of cassava paste. In the Amazon, cassava also makes bread and farofa (a fried dish).

A TIPITI

REAL MEDICINE MEN AND WOMEN

Francisco Montes Shuna and Yolanda Panduro Baneo from Peru painted pictures to show the spirits they see in rainforest plants.

SEE THIS ON THE TOP PATH

UNDER THE ARCH TO THE BOAT-SHAPED FLOWERBED WITH COLA AND CHICLE ... THEN RUBBER ON

CROPS AND CULTIVATION

COLA (H.08) AND GUM (H.07)

Enid finds the chicle tree for chewing gum and a cola tree that makes cola drink in the boat-shaped flowerbed.

CHICLE TREE

COLA TREE

THIS SIDE SHOWS YOU THE PRODUCTS

DIGGER MATCHES THEM UP

Help me match the plant to the product below. You'll find all these plants as you go round the rest of the Biome.

Cocoa, Coffee, Cashew, Cola nut, Banana, Ginger

packet of cashew nuts, banana split, chocolate bar, gingerbread man, cola bottle, coffee pot

THIS SIDE OF THE ARCH SHOWS YOU THE PLANTS

YOUR LEFT... AND A NEW RAINFOREST GROWING AT THE BOTTOM OF THE STEPS (COCOA TOO!).

RUBBER BOOTS

RUBBER (H.09)

Rubber is made from a white, sticky liquid called latex. The rubber tapper cuts the tree carefully and collects the latex in a cup. Millions of rubber trees have been planted in Malaysia, Indonesia and other tropical countries. Alan makes the rubber he finds into tyres and rubber gloves.

LATEX BEING COLLECTED FROM A RUBBER TREE

The Eden project is a charity. The money spent here helps support education on site and projects like FORRU. Hey, Enid, did you pay to get in?

TREE NURSERY IN FORRU PROJECT

RE-GROWING THE FOREST (H.10)

An area of rainforest the size of a UK football pitch (0.6ha) is cut down every 1.5 seconds. Eek! But...Eden works with the Forest Restoration Research Unit (FORRU) in Thailand, where scientists and local people are reversing the trend.

AFTER THE RUBBER, COCOA TREES ON YOUR RIGHT, COCONUTS ON YOUR LEFT AND FURTHER ON

HOW DOES CHOCOLATE GROW?

COCOA (H.11)

The beans inside the huge orange pods are fermented, dried and taken across the world to make chocolate. The cocoa growers are breeding cocoa trees that resist disease so they don't have to spray them with chemicals. That's a relief!

ENID CAN MAKE CHOCOLATE FROM COCOA BEANS

Some chocolate is organic, some is Fairtrade. Alan, check out the label. Your wallet is your weapon.

CHOCOLATE (H.11)

Nip down the steps and take a look at the cartoons to find out all about the history of chocolate in our Mayeux tapestry. Who did the Aztec emperor, Montezuma, give the chocolate to? C_____.

THE MAYEUX TAPESTRY

LOTS OF DIFFERENT TYPES OF PALM TREES, INCLUDING OIL PALMS.

PALM TREES GALORE

A BABY COCONUT PALM TREE

COCONUT (H.12)

Sweets, coconut milk, doormats, face cream, food and potting compost are all made from coconut palms. Useful plant!

OIL PALM (H.12)

Alan's spotted the oil palms. Oil from their seeds is used in cakes and pies, for frying and in soap and make-up. The palms produce oil for people all over the world.

OIL DRUMS

DIGGER DIGS DEEPER (H.12)

Millions of oil palms have been planted in the tropics in place of the rainforests where orang-utans lived. People are now working to save the orang-utan and the forest they live in, and to find better ways to produce palm oil.

SAVE THE ORANG-UTAN

FOOD TRAIL

H.12

WHAT AM I?

CROSS ME WITH SILVER,
FOUND IN A PIE
AND CAKES AND
PASTRIES AND LOADS
OF STUFF.
OH MY, OH MY, OH MY!

PAST COFFEE ON YOUR RIGHT. LOOK TO YOUR LEFT FOR SUGAR CANE, AND THE TRUCK, THEN BANANA

WHAT'S IN A CUP OF SWEET COFFEE?

COFFEE (H.13)

Coffee beans are found inside red coffee 'cherries'. These are often picked by hand rather than machine as they don't ripen all at once.

COFFEE 'CHERRIES'

THE COFFEE STAND

SUGAR CANE (H.14)

Sugar cane, a type of thick-stemmed tropical grass, is full of natural sugar. The canes are crushed and the sugar extracted with water.

Sugar may be tasty but I don't touch it. It wrecks my teeth. Digger says eat bananas instead. Personally I prefer raw fish!

SUGAR TRUCK

...ROUND THE BEND TO ...TROPICAL FRUITS.

A RIGHT FRUIT SALAD!

MANGOES (H.15)

Eating mangoes can be messy because they are so juicy. Sucking the stone is the best bit!

BANANAS (H.16)

Digger visits the hut.

BANANAS GROWING

DIGGER GETS A REALLY HEALTHY BOOST!

Sportspeople eat loads of bananas because the energy you get from them lasts for ages. Take a look at the quiz round the back of the banana hut (the top shelter amongst the bananas).

TROPICAL FRUIT (H.17)

Have you tasted açaí, papaya or lychee? What's your favourite? Find out more about them on the fruit tables.

FRUIT TABLES

FOOD TRAIL

H.16

H.17

PAST THE BAMBOO HOUSE, BIOFUELS AND PINEAPPLES ON THE RIGHT. THEN THE SWEET SCENT OF

MATERIALS, FUEL AND A TASTY TREAT

A HUMAN 'MONKEY' IN THE BAMBOO HOUSE

BAMBOO (H.18)

Half the world's people use bamboo for homes, furniture, food, fuel, music and medicine. What things could Alan and Enid use from the bamboo house?

PINEAPPLE

PINEAPPLES (H.20)

Enid can't find the pineapple trees. Why do you think that is? Because they grow on strange spiky plants near the ground. How weird!

SPICES BEFORE NUTS AND LIFE IN THE TREETOPS. PHEW! TIME TO GO BACK OUT AND COOL OFF.

NUTS AND SPICES

DISCOVERING CLUES IN THE SPICE BOAT

NUTS (H.22)

Cashews hang below these large, red, pear-shaped fruits on the cashew tree. The shells contain corrosive cashew-nut shell liquor (CNSL). This makes shelling them very tricky. This CNSL is used to make heatproof paints and car brake pads!

CASHEW NUT

PEPPER (H.21)

White and black peppercorns come from the red fruits of a climbing vine from tropical Asia. Black peppercorns are made by drying the unripe fruits. White peppercorns are made by removing the red skin first.

DIGGER ASKS:

(H.21)

What spice put America on the map?

Why are Cornish buns yellow?

Explore the drawers in the spice boat to find the answers. If you're stuck, ask one of the Eden team.

A PEPPER VINE

ACTIVITY PAGE

SIMPLE CROSSWORD

1. The dog with an appetite: ______
2. The tree that makes our wellies: ______
3. The plant that makes chocolate: _____
4. The giant robot made of rubbish: _______
5. The plant with seeds like a giant bottom: ____ __ ___
6. The fruit that sportspeople like: ______

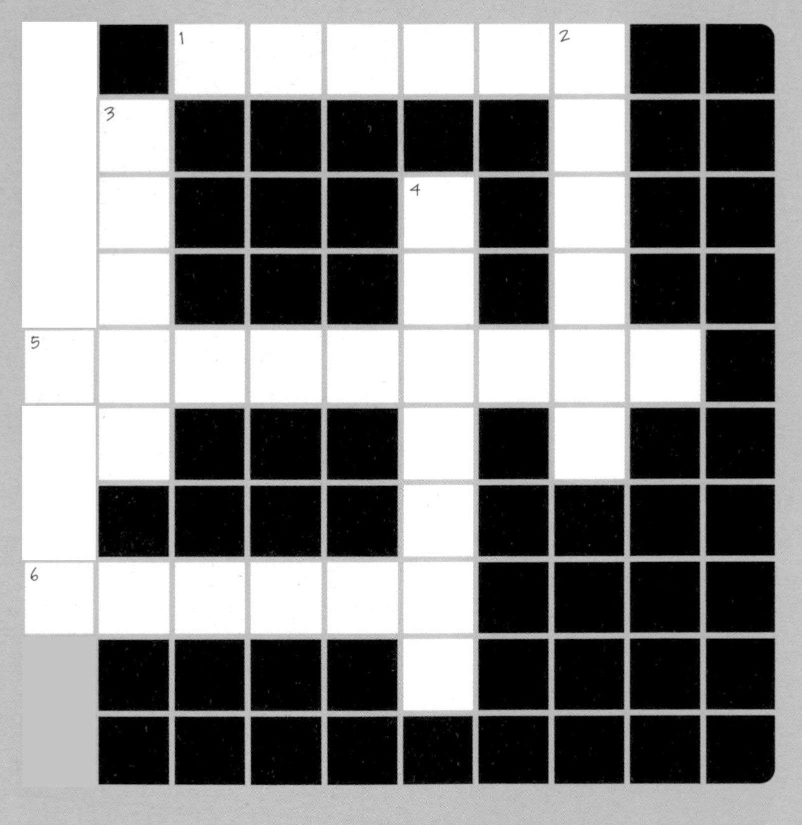

(Answers at the back of the book.)

I SPY IN THE LINK:

We took 6 photos in the Link . . . close-ups! Tick them off when you spot them.

(If you get stuck ask one of the Eden team.)

THE
MEDITERRANEAN
BIOME

WALK TO THE GOLDEN PATH, THROUGH SCENTED HERBS AND GNARLED OLIVES. PAST THE VINES AND

WELCOME TO THE MEDITERRANEAN REGIONS

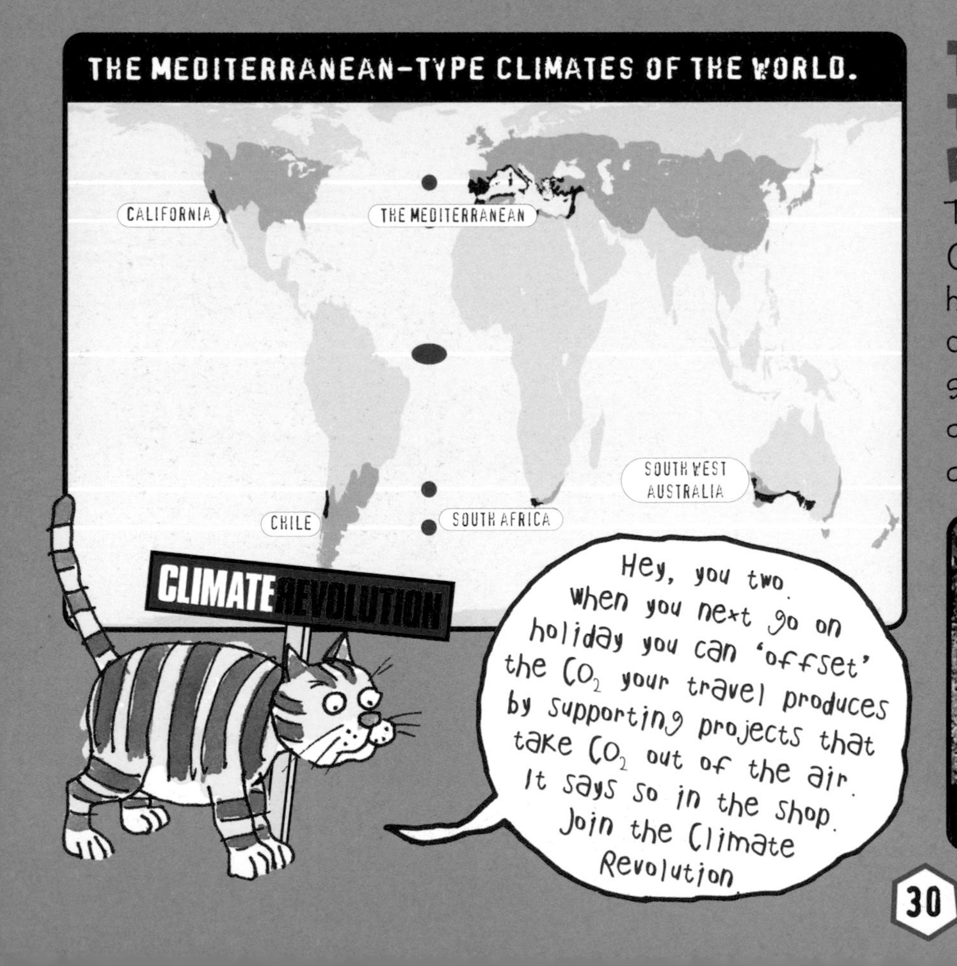

THE WARM TEMPERATE REGIONS (W.01)

The Mediterranean, California and South Africa have hot, dry summers and cool, wet winters. We use sun cream and sun hats and drink cool drinks if we go on holiday here.

ROSEMARY PLANT

SCENTED THYME

SUN FACTOR (W.01)

The plants avoid sunburn and thirst by having waxy or hairy leaves and scented oils. Look at the size of their leaves compared to the Rainforest Biome plants. Why do you reckon they are smaller?

DANCING METAL FIGURES TO THE CAROB TREE AND FIG TREE WHERE THE PATHS MEET.

THE OLIVE OIL PATH

THE MEDITERRANEAN (W.02)

Enid loves her Mediterranean food: some olive oil, a few herbs. On the path behind her you can see some doves, one for each Mediterranean country which grows olives. How many can you count?

(Answers at the back of the book.)

FOOD FACTS FROM A FRIENDLY DOG

Before you go off to find your food trail stamps, chew on this!
Two fruits, two facts.
Which goes with which?

- The flowers are found on the inside of these fruits and they are pollinated by tiny wasps. Bzzz!
- These fruits have a crown at their tip. You can get out the fiddly seeds by cutting the fruit in half, putting them face down and bashing with a spoon. Messy!

FIG

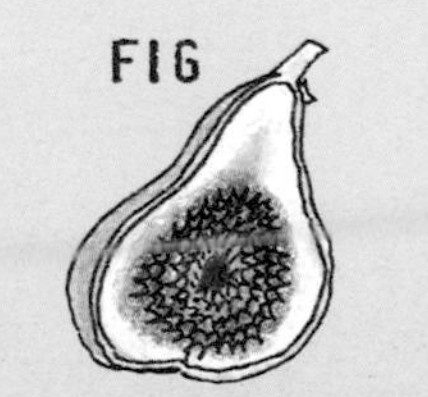

POMEGRANATE

THE CAROB TREE (W.02)

Its seeds, used to make a chocolate substitute, are also called locust beans. Some say that John the Baptist ate these during his 40 days in the desert, not real locusts at all!

THE CAROB TREE

VISIT SOUTH AFRICA . . .

FIRE FLOWERS

BIRD-LIKE PROTEAS

THE FYNBOS FIRE FLOWERS

(W.03)

There are loads of really unusual and rare plants in this part of South Africa. Sometimes these really dry areas go up in flames. New plants grow out of the burned earth.

NAMAQUALAND

(W.03)

In these dry desert areas, flowers appear like a multicoloured carpet after it rains.

Eden works with Green Futures College, South Africa. Students from poor areas get jobs looking after the rare plants.

DRY DESERT | DRY DESERT | DRY DESERT | DRY DESERT

DRY DESERT | RAIN | PLINK | DAISIES

. . . AND CALIFORNIA

ALAN FINDS HIS AGAVE (W.04)

Spiky leaves with long fibres for brushes, sacking and twine. Their flowers make soap and their sap a boozy drink: tequila.

AGAVE, A VERY USEFUL PLANT

COWBOYS

The plants in the 'chaparral' are tough and spiky. Horse riders wear 'chaps' to protect their legs.

INDIANS

The Native Americans who reached California about 15,000 years ago found so many wild plants and animals to eat that they had no need to develop farming.

DIGGER UPDATES US

Times change. Today California has hundreds of farms growing fruits and vegetables . . . and now petrol-driven horses have taken over.

HARLEY DAVIDSON

IDEAS FOR TOMORROW

People all over the world are now working on ideas for getting fuel from plants and energy from the sun and wind . . . hurrah! Send your ideas to **sniff@edenproject.com**

FOLLOW THE PATH ROUND, THROUGH THE POLYTUNNEL ARCH. SPOT THE CORK PIGS ON YOUR RIGHT

CROPS AND CULTIVATION

WE GROW DIFFERENT CROPS HERE AT DIFFERENT TIMES OF YEAR. WHAT CAN YOU SEE IN THE GROUND TODAY?

CROPS FOR SHOPS (W.05)

In these sunny places just add water and plant fertilizer and . . . fruits and vegetables grow, grow, grow. The water isn't going to last for ever so farmers and scientists are exploring clever ways of growing their crops using less water.

Buying cork helps the cork forests and the plants, animals and people that depend on them. Alan, we need to talk cork!

WHAT A CORKER (W.06)

Usually land either grows wild plants or crops. Cork forests do both! They produce a crop to sell (cork from the tree bark), ham to eat (from pigs that eat acorns) and provide a home for many wild creatures . . . good for everyone!

CORK PIG

POP

PLASTIC

CORKS: GOOD FOR THE BIRDS

AND TREES ON YOUR LEFT. IN THE SUMMER THESE TREES ARE COVERED IN FRUITS.

VITAMIN C CITY!

SUNNY FRUITS (W.07)

Peach or kiwi. Which fact for which fruit?

FACT: These fruits have fuzzy skins and are related to almonds. They are full of Vitamin C. Do you know what that's good for?

FACT: Named after a bird from New Zealand that can't fly. Also called the Chinese gooseberry because this is where it really comes from.

KIWI FRUIT

PEACH

DIGGER GETS HOT ON PEPPERS (W.08)

There's pepper – as in salt and pepper – and these. These peppers are fruits and they are vegetables. You can cook them or put them in the fruit bowl and eat them like apples. Like the other fruits here they are full of Vitamin C, which keeps colds and spots at bay. Some peppers are cool, and some are hot, hot, hot! Which is your favourite?

GO TO THE CITRUS GROVE, WHERE YOU CAN SOMETIMES LISTEN TO A STORY, AND ON TOWARDS THE

ORANGES AND LEMONS

AND LIMES AND CITRONS AND . . . (W.10)

Enid loves citrus fruit: 'So many to choose from.' How many can you name?

1. A thirst-quenching drink, we make it at Eden: L____ade
2. A green one similar in shape to 1: L___
3. One shaped like a yellow rubber glove: the B_____s hand
4. The answer to the food trail riddle W.10: O_____
5. The largest member of this family: C____n
6. Mandarin, tangerine, oh my darling C_________
7. Your turn: find another you've never seen before.

Take a closer look at the trees for more clues and if you get stuck, ask a member of the Eden team.

You can buy organic fruit (good for the environment) and Fairtrade fruit (gives a fair deal to the people that grow it). Enid, have you checked the labels?

MORE THAN TASTY! (W.10)

Citrus oils are used as flavourings and in scents and cleaning products.

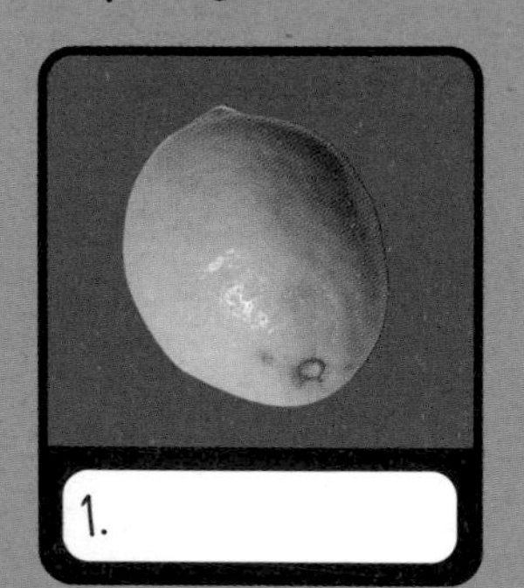

1.

2.

3.

4. orange

5.

6.

(Answers at the back of the book.)

BIG BULL (DIONYSUS). LOOK FOR GRAPES GROWING IN AUTUMN.

DIONYSUS AND THE VINES

The big bronze bull, Dionysus, started life as god of nature and gardening in Greek mythology. He then got keen on one plant – the grape, and the drink it made: wine – and then look what happened. Things got a little out of control!

DIGGER RUNS IN CIRCLES

There are three stamps and three riddles to collect. Here's one:

What are we?
Jellied, dried or juiced,
Or trampled with bare feet
To make wines from vines.
Hic! Dry or sweet? (W.11)

GRAPES

THE VINES GROW NEW LEAVES EVERY SPRING AND NEW GRAPES EVERY AUTUMN

FOOD TRAIL

W.09

W.10

W.11

TAKE A LOOK ROUND THE BEDS IN THIS SECTION . . . EVERY SEASON BRINGS NEW

CROPS AND THEIR STORIES

The exhibits in this section change every year so apologies if things have moved.

COTTON

COTTON IS SPUN INTO THREAD THEN WOVEN INTO CLOTH

NEW WAYS TO WATER

TEMPORARY DISPLAYS (W.12)

In the spring you'll see bulbs.
In the summer, cotton and tobacco, both connected to the slave trade.
In the winter, the prickly pear cactus with tasty fruits.

GROWING SYSTEMS (W.14)

There's loads of water in the world. Trouble is, most of it's salty and plants don't like salt. Fresh water is getting scarcer. Eden is working with people who are making fresh water out of sea water!

CUT FLOWERS (W.13)

Some have labels saying where they came from so you can check out flower miles (the more miles the more CO_2 pollution). Some carry a Fairtrade label too.

ROSES

SURPRISES. THEN ON TO THE OLIVE JARS AND PERFUME WALL TO THE RIGHT.

WHICH SCENT IS WHICH?

PERFUME (W.16)

Why do some flowers have perfume? To attract bees and other insects which pollinate them so they can make seeds. Why do you think some people wear perfume?

OLIVE OIL

(W.15)

Olive oil is supposed to be one of the best, a true superfood: good for the heart, good for keeping the blood vessels clean.

OLIVES

TAKE A LOOK IN THE OLIVE JARS

OILY DIGGER (W.15)

People living in the Mediterranean have been known to drink it for breakfast. Find out 2 more things about olive oil in the olive jars.

1. ________________________________
2. ________________________________

FOOD TRAIL

W.15

WHAT AM I?

I GROW ON SMALL-LEAVED TREES,
CAN BE PICKED AND STORED IN A TIN.
I'M BETTER KNOWN AS A HEALTH-GIVING OIL,
NOW USED AS FOOD BUT ONCE PUT ON SKIN.

ACTIVITY PAGE

colour me in

SUNNY WORDSEARCH

Find the following plants in the wordsearch and when you find them in the Biome, colour in the word too. Good luck!

THYME
CAROB
POMEGRANATE
PROTEA
SAGE
AGAVE
CORK
KIWI FRUIT
PEACH
TOBACCO
PEPPER
ORANGE
GRAPE
TOMATO
ONION
AUBERGINE
OLIVE

E	O	L	I	V	E	K	A	E	G
T	N	P	R	B	P	V	T	P	T
A	I	R	M	E	G	N	A	R	O
N	N	U	P	K	P	W	U	G	M
A	C	A	R	O	B	P	B	P	A
R	R	O	O	F	S	O	E	R	T
G	C	E	R	A	I	A	R	P	O
E	M	Y	H	T	C	W	G	I	N
M	C	N	C	H	S	I	I	E	I
O	C	C	A	B	O	T	N	K	O
P	R	O	T	E	A	T	E	E	N

SPOT THE DIFFERENCE

Find the 6 differences between the 2 pictures.

HIDDEN GECKOS

How many geckos can you see scooting around the page? ....

(Answers at the back of the book.)

THE CORE

Wow, the whole world in a bubble!
TAKE A LOOK AT THE JARS ON THE GROUND FLOOR. VISIT THE INNER CHAMBER TO SEE THE GIANT
WELCOME TO THE CORE
Come on in and explore Eden's Education Centre, the shape of a sunflower head and the size of a spaceship, containing a magical world of adventures.
Tricky one! Find my skeleton in an exhibit. Email sniff@edenproject.com
The glass jars show how plants look after our world – and us! Which jar shows what?
☐ Plants make fresh air for us to breathe
☐ They keep our climate under control
☐ They recycle our waste
☐ They support animals
☐ They clean our water
☐ They give us ideas to copy (biomimicry)
☐ They suck CO_2 out of the air
☐ They give us inspiration
THE PLANT ENGINE THAT KEEPS US ALIVE
JAR 1
JAR 2
JAR 3
JAR 4
JAR 5
JAR 6
JAR 7
JAR 8

Fancy a STRAWBERRY, Alan?

Vitami A

Esse

SEED. GO UPSTAIRS TO EXPLORE BIOMIMICRY AND JO'S SUPERFOODS CAFÉ.

FRIDGE WALL

THE GIANT 75-TONNE SEED, SCULPTED FROM CORNISH GRANITE, SITS IN THE INNER CHAMBER

DIGGER FINDS JO'S CAFÉ!

The café upstairs has loads of jars showing you which foods give you which vitamins and minerals. You can draw your favourite food on the blackboard. Mine's a bone!

TICK THEM WHEN YOU'VE DONE THEM!

☐ Use the biggest nutcracker in the world.

☐ Guess the next numbers – 0 1 1 2 3 5 8 13 21 _ _ *. (The spirals that go to the left and to the right in sunflowers, pineapples and our roof, are two consecutive numbers in this sequence.)

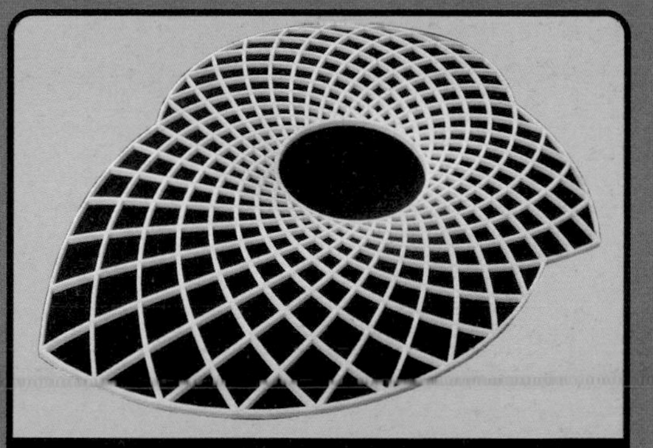

COUNT HOW MANY SPIRALS THERE ARE IN EACH DIRECTION

*(Each number is the sum of the previous two.)

GARDENS ROUND THE CORE

HEALTH (0.25)

Enid's found her medicine cupboard: rows and rows of plants that are used to make our medicines. Do you recognize any?

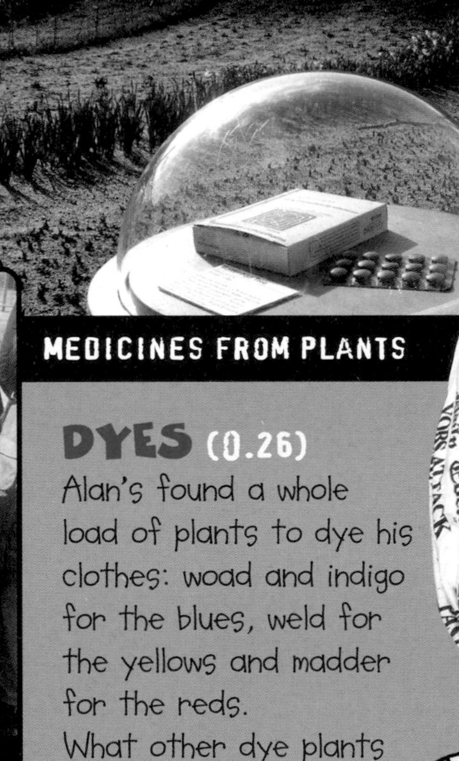
MEDICINES FROM PLANTS

INDIGO DYE WORKSHOP

DYES (0.26)

Alan's found a whole load of plants to dye his clothes: woad and indigo for the blues, weld for the yellows and madder for the reds.
What other dye plants can you find?

PAPER (0.27)

Paper usually comes from trees but can also be made from all the plants you see growing here.

PAPER FROM CLOTHES AND CLOTHES FROM PAPER

Use your head - save paper. Write on both sides, recycle it, use recycled paper and buy paper made from sustainably produced wood - look on the label.

OR UP THE STEPS TO THE ARCADE OF IDEAS. TRY YOUR SKILLS ON THE DANCE MAT GAME.

THE SPIRAL GARDEN (0.28)

Loads of ideas in here for your own gardens and a growing spiral made from willow.

- Make a rainbow in flowers
- Make a mosaic out of broken china
- Grow the pitcher plant that eats flies.
- Find out more about our *'Mud Between Your Toes'* programme.

FLY CATCHER

THE SPIRAL GARDEN

TIMBER (0.29)

Boats, oars, chairs, doors, homes, piles, sticks to walk miles, frames for Morgans, pipes for organs, artificial legs and tent pegs.
See which wood is best for what.

RED SPRUCE BROUGHT US THE FRAME OF THE CORE

DIGGER VISITS THE ARCADE OF IDEAS (0.30)

I'm going up the lift to an amusement arcade with a difference. My favourite things are the tractors. Take a ride and find your breakfast! Fancy bacon? Find the pig!

EDEN - THE FACTS

BIGGEST WATER PLANT LEAF
at Eden: Victorian giant water lily, Rainforest Biome.

BIG PITCH
In the beginning the disused china clay pit was 60m deep. It is the same area as 35 football pitches.

HUGE
There are 625 hexagons in all, the largest being 11 metres across.

DISASTER!
43 million gallons of water raining into the pit in 90 days meant that our engineers had to come up with a fantastic drainage system right from the start.

LARGEST
flowering plant at Eden: Titan Arum, Rainforest Biome.

SIZE
The world's largest conservatories weigh only slightly more than the air they contain. The Tower of London could fit inside the Rainforest Biome.

SCORCHING
Unlike glass, the ETFE that covers the Biomes transmits ultraviolet rays, which means you can get a suntan indoors. Don't forget to cover up.

COPPER
The roof of the Core is covered with copper, 0.6mm thick, and was responsibly sourced from one mine in America.

BUBBLES
Three layers of ETFE (ethylenetetrafluoroethylene) transparent foil form inflated pillows 2m deep in each of the hexagons. ETFE weighs less than 1% of the same area of glass.

SOIL
In a pit with no soil the team had to make their own – 83,000 tonnes of it – using china clay waste and organic waste. The compost heap to beat them all!

HOW MANY PLANTS?
In 2006 over 552,667 plants, of approximately 3812 species.

TALLEST
tree in the Rainforest Biome: the kapok tree at over 26.6m.

SOLAR POWER
The Core is powered partly by the sun.

ON YOUR JOURNEY DID YOU SPOT

DID YOU SPOT?

A secret door
Teeth made of mice
A horse in a jar
Some chocolate cartoons
Some African Totems
A path of gold
A Harley motorbike

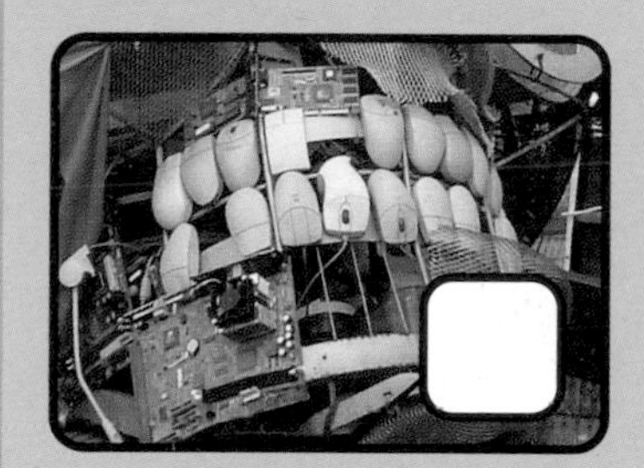

IF YOU'VE DONE IT, TICK THE BOX

- ☐ Made something in a workshop
- ☐ Listened to a story
- ☐ Recycled some rubbish in the bins
- ☐ Walked the labyrinth in Myth and Folklore **(O.22)**.

If not, don't despair, here's how to draw your own!

The labyrinth in Myth and Folklore is based on an ancient classical labyrinth. A single path loops around to make seven paths to the central goal.

You can draw a seven-circuit labyrinth like this one. It is based on a 'seed pattern'. The seed pattern is a cross with four right angles within the ones created by the cross, and a dot in each right angle.

Start at the top of the cross, draw a curved line to join it to the first available line or dot. Keep going until you have the whole labyrinth.

THE EDEN TRAIL
A CHILDREN'S GUIDE BOOK
AN EDEN PROJECT BOOK 978 1 905 81115 1

Published in Great Britain by Eden Project Books,
an imprint of Transworld Publishers
A Random House Group Company

This edition published 2007

11

Inset illustrations on pages 2, 7, 9, 20, 32, 34, 35 by Alan Clarke
Designed by Helen McDonagh
Site map prepared by Gendall Design

The Random House Group Limited makes every effort to ensure that the
papers in its books are made from trees that have been legally sourced from
well-managed and credibly certified forests.
Our paper procurement policy can be found at:
www.randomhouse.co.uk/paper.htm

TRANSWORLD PUBLISHERS
61-63 Uxbridge Road, London W5 5SA

www.edenproject.com
www.kidsatrandomhouse.co.uk

Addresses for companies within The Random House Group Limited
can be found at: www.randomhouse.co.uk/offices.htm

THE RANDOM HOUSE GROUP Limited Reg. No. 954009

A CIP catalogue record for this book is available from the
British Library.

The Eden Project is owned by the Eden Trust,
A registered charity.
Eden Project, Bodelva, St Austell, Cornwall PL24 2SG

Printed and bound in Italy

ANSWERS TO PUZZLES

THE RAINFOREST BIOME

Page 15: sugar cane, coffee beans, cocoa, bananas, mangoes.

Page 28:

1 = Digger
2 = rubber
3 = cocoa
4 = weeeman
5 = coco de mer
6 = banana

THE MEDITERRANEAN BIOME

Page 31: 22 doves

Page 36:

1. lemon
2. lime
3. buddha
4. orange
5. citron
6. clementine

Page 40:
11 geckos

Page 40: Wordsearch; we keep a filled in copy at the information kiosk in the Link.

Page 40: Spot the difference

1. spots on jar
2. olive missing off tree
3. little flower missing by Alan's elbow
4. Alan sniffing olive instead of flower
5. flowers missing in background above Alan's right hand
6. leaf missing in foreground (in front of Alan's chest)

THE CORE

Page 42:

Plants make fresh air for us to breathe (6)
They keep our climate under control (5)
They recycle our waste (7)
They support other life forms (3)
They clean our water (8)
The give us ideas to copy (biomimicry) (4)
The suck CO_2 out of the air (1)
They give us inspiration (2)

For any answers we couldn't fit in here ask a member of the Eden team.

Don't forget to send in your riddle answers and your ideas to help the planet to the address or email on page 2.